The Maso~~n Bees~~

Taking the sting out of Bee-keeping

A practical guide for
gardeners and fruit growers
to the propagation and
management of *Osmia lignaria,*
and its relatives, docile and
efficient pollinators

by

Christopher O'Toole

(Head of Bee Systematics and Biology Unit,
Hope Entomological Collections,
Oxford University Museum of Natural History,
Oxford, UK)

Osmia **Publications, Banbury**

First published in 2001 by *Osmia* Publications, Banbury, UK

© *Osmia* Publications 2001

ISBN 0-9539906-3-X

A CIP record for this title is available from the British Library.

Cover Photograph: A female Blue orchard Mason Bee, *Osmia lignaria*. © Scott Bauer/USDA-ARS Photo Unit.

Production by *Osmia* Publications

Designed by Louisa Stevens

Printed and bound in Thailand by Gift Export Co. Ltd

About the Author

Chris O'Toole has been studying wild bees for more than 30 years. He heads the Bee Systematics and Biology Unit at the Oxford University Museum of Natural History and is the author of many papers and book on insects, especially bees. He is also a frequent broadcaster on radio and has been involved in the production of many television programs in natural history, most notably the BBCtv series *Alien Empire,* for which he wrote the accompanying book of the same name.

His research interests include the nesting biology of the European Red Mason Bee, *Osmia rufa* and the systematics, biogeography and floral relations of Mediterranean bees.

Chris O'Toole is the founder of the Oxford Bee Company Ltd., a spinout company of Oxford University.

Acknowledgements

I thank my wife Rose for her constant support and encouragement and for holding the vision of Oxford Bee Company Ltd. I also thank Dr Peter Hotten of Isis Innovation Ltd, the technology transfer company of Oxford University, for facilitating the gestation and final delivery of OBC.

I am indebted to Larry Snell for making available his wisdom and skills in the business world and for having the courage to invest his life in the OBC.

I am grateful Prof Stephen J. Simpson, Curator of the Hope Entomological Collections of the University Museum for his interest in and support of Oxford Bee Company Ltd.

I thank Graham Kinsman of Kinsman Company Inc for stimulating the writing of this book.

The excellent illustrations of this book are a tribute to the skills of several photographers. I thank the US Department of Agriculture ARS and their photographic archive and also Dr Karen Strickler for the generosity of spirit behind the complimentary use of their photographs, which are acknowledged in the individual captions. I also thank Rod and Ken Preston-Mafham of Premaphotos Wildlife and my brother, Peter O'Toole. I thank, too, my old friend and fellow bee enthusiast, Dr Anthony Raw, not only for two excellent photographs, but also for stimulating my interest in *Osmia rufa* all those years ago.

Finally, I thank all those friends and relatives who have allowed me to use their gardens as propagation plots for mason bees; they have contributed much to my education.

Christopher O'Toole

Contents

The Color Plates

Plate 1
A female *Blue Orchard Mason Bee*, Osmia lignaria.© *Scott Bauer/USDA-ARS Photo Unit.*

Plate 2
A worker honeybee, *Apis milliner*, at apple blossom, with nearly full pollen baskets. © *Ken Preston-Mafham, Premaphotos Wildlife.*

Plate 3
A female *Horn-faced Mason Bee*, Osmia cornifrons, *with a full pollen load in her abdominal scopa, resting on a leaf.* © *Karen Strickler.*

Plate 4
A worker of the European Garden Bumblebee, Bombus hortorum, *uses its long tongue to probe for nectar in the deep, tubular flower of a primrose, Primula vulgaris. North American bumblebees with equally long tongues include Bombus fervidus and B. vagans. In such species, tongues can be 75-80% of body length.* © *Ken Preston-Mafham, Premaphotos Wildlife.*

Plate 5
Emerging from her 'quarry', a female of the European Red Mason Bee, Osmia rufa, *bears a glistening pellet of mud between her jaws, ready for use back at her nest.* © *Ken Preston-Mafham, Premaphotos Wildlife.*

Plate 6
Carrying her ball of mud, a female of the European Red Mason Bee, Osmia rufa *returns to her nest in an old garden cane. Note one of the pair of stout horns beneath the antennae with which she presses her mud into the desired shape inside the nest. You can also see the dense scopa or fringe of specialized pollen-transporting hairs on the underside of her abdomen.* © *Dr Rod Preston-Mafham, Premaphotos Wildlife.*

Plate 7
Four completed cells of the European Red Mason Bee, Osmia rufa, *each with a pearly white egg on its pollen store. Note the mud partitions between each cell. A section through the nest of Osmia lignaria, its North American close relative, would look identical.* © *Anthony Raw*

Plate 8
Nearly full-grown larvae of the European Red Mason Bee, Osmia rufa, *feeding on pollen.* © *Anthony Raw*

Plate 9
A pupal cocoon of the European Red Mason Bee, Osmia rufa, *opened to expose the larvae of the parasitic wasp, Monodontomerus obscurus, which have eaten the bee pupa. In North America, this wasp parasitizes the Blue Orchard Mason Bee, Osmia lignaria, O. cordata and the Alfalfa Leafcutter Bee, Megachile rotundata.* © *C. O'Toole*

Plate 10
A female of the Alfalfa Leafcutter Bee, Megachile rotundata, *at alfalfa flowers, Medicago sativa.* © *Karen Strickler.*

Plate 11
A trailer-mounted field shelter containing thousands of nests of the Alfalfa Leafcutter bee, Megachile rotundata, *in an alfalfa field, Cache Valley, Utah.* © *C. O'Toole*

Plate 12
A female of a native North American mason bee, Osmia ribifloris, *which has potential as a managed pollinator of highbush blueberry. This female is feeding at flowers of barberry (Berberis sp.).* © *Jack Dykinga, USDA-ARS Photo Unit.*

Plate 13
Nester kits for mason bees from the Oxford Bee Co. © *Peter O'Toole*

Plate 14
Nester kit for mason bees attached to wooden fence with plastic pipe bracket.
© *Peter O'Toole*

ONE

Blue Orchard Mason Bees as pollination pets

There is a growing realization that backyards and garden plots can be havens for wildlife: they can attract much of the diversity of life to be found in the neighborhood.

Perhaps you have already helped by planting a range of flowers and shrubs attractive to birds, butterflies and bees. We are all familiar with the idea of putting out nest boxes for birds. It is a delight to watch, say, a pair of titmice or chickadees rearing their young through spring and there is a real satisfaction to be had in knowing that one is providing a home for these lovely creatures, a feeling of being involved in the conservation of wildlife.

Now it is possible to do the same for a really useful and pretty little insect, the Blue Orchard Mason bee, *Osmia lignaria* (Front cover, Plate 1). As well as helping in the conservation of these important insects, there is now an opportunity to play an active role in managing the pollination ecology of your backyard garden plot or orchard.

With the nester kits described below, you can become a bee rancher and see increased yields in your fruit and vegetable crops. *Osmia lignaria* will readily use the nests and you can enjoy watching your bees returning with pollen to the homes you have provided. And you don't have to get dressed up in protective suits and veils. *Osmia lignaria* takes the sting out of beekeeping and is a docile but hard working bee and thus an ideal pollination pet for the garden. Furthermore, unlike the honeybee, *Osmia lignaria* is not host to the parasitic mite *Varroa* which has wrought such havoc in beehives all over the USA.

While this book is mostly about *Osmia lignaria* and the nesters you can use to attract them, it also covers a number of related bee species which might also take up lodging in the homes you provide.

Pollination: Nature's Market Place
Flowering Plants – the producers

Like us, flowering plants are sexual organisms and pollination is the process by which male cells, pollen, are transferred from the male organs, the anthers, to the stigma, the receptive, female part of the flower. Most flowering plants are self-incompatible, that is, each must receive pollen from another individual plant of the same species if fertilization and seed set is to occur.

Being rooted, literally, to the spot, plants need some agent to help them transport pollen from one individual to another. Some, such as pines, oaks, willows and grasses are adapted for pollination by wind: they produce billions of very tiny light pollen grains from very exposed flowers. However, the majority of flowering plants are pollinated by insects and have evolved various ways and means of recruiting them for the business of mating by proxy. The impact of a flower rich garden which we humans find so attractive, with its brightly colored petals and sweet scents, evolved to attract insects, especially bees.

We can liken the relationship between flowering plants and bees to a market place, where retailers (the plants) use color and scent to advertise their wares (pollen and nectar) to a band of more or less discriminating consumers (the bees). This economy is based on two currencies, energy and time. And both partners have to invest some of this currency in order to buy themselves into the market. The plants expend time and energy in advertising and manufacturing pollen and nectar, and the female bees have already invested time and energy in mating, seeking and building a nest before they venture into the market place.

Nectar is an energy rich mixture of sugars which fuels the bees' activities and which some, such as the honeybee and bumblebees, convert into honey which they store as a source of energy. And pollen is rich in protein and minerals. Plants produce amounts in excess of those required for reproduction, this excess being an offered reward for the bee's pollinating services.

Bees – the consumers

Bees are a group of hunting wasps which became vegetarians. Instead of insect prey, they gather pollen as a source of protein for their larvae. In scrabbling about for pollen, a female bee becomes dusted with hundreds of thousand of pollen grains. When she next visits a plant of the same species, some of these pollen grains inevitably get brushed off onto the receptive female part of the flower, the stigma: pollination and, eventually, fertilization is accomplished.

Bees have evolved a number of adaptations to exploit the resources on offer by plants. They are densely clothed with branched, feathery hairs which easily trap pollen and they have structures for the transport of consolidated masses of pollen. Some, such as the honeybees and bumblebees, have a pollen basket on the outer face of the hind leg (Plate 2). This takes the form of an expanded and slightly concave surface fringed with stiff bristles. The bees use their legs to remove pollen from the body hairs and pass it back to the hind legs. Here, mixed with a little nectar to make it sticky, they build it up to form a solid mass.

Other bees such as the mining bees, which nest in the ground, have a dense brush of specialized hairs on the hind legs called the scopa. Here they consolidate a rather dry mass of pollen. The leaf-cutter bees (*Megachile* spp.) and mason bees, (*Osmia* spp.), have their scopa in the form of dense fringes of stiff hairs on the underside of the abdomen (Plates 3 and 6).

Bees have also evolved longer tongues so that they can probe deep-tubed flowers for nectar (Plate 4).

The bee-flower relationship is a co-evolved partnership which took millions of years to refine and much of life on this planet is directly dependent on it. Indeed, every third mouthful of human food is dependent on the pollination services of bees. And you can benefit directly from this partnership by keeping the Blue Orchard Mason bee in your own backyard or orchard. They are fun and easy to keep, safe with children and pets and you will be helping in the conservation of ecologically important insects.

TWO

The natural History of the Blue Orchard Mason bee, *Osmia lignaria*

Life history

Osmia lignaria is a spring bee. Depending on where you live in North America, it may make its first appearance in late March or mid-April. Both sexes are a dark metallic blue in color and are clothed with black hairs and dark, smoky wings; in some populations, there are pale hairs on the sides of the thorax and the base of the abdomen (Front cover & Plate 1). The bees are active from April to June, slightly later in southern hilly areas and southern Canada.

This bee is a solitary species. That is, each nest is the work of a single female, working alone; there is no co-operating caste of workers such as are found in the social honeybee and bumblebees. In fact, these familiar bees are in a distinct minority: the vast majority of bees are solitary just like *O. lignaria*. Unlike the social bees, there is no overlap of generations: a female solitary bee never lives to see her offspring.

Although *O. lignaria* is a solitary bee, it is gregarious. In other words, if there are enough nest holes to go round, nesting females attract other females and you may have many females nesting close together.

Most solitary bees are mining bees, which excavate nest tunnels and brood cells in the ground. The females of these bees line their cells with a glandular secretion which is waterproof and resistant to bacteria and fungi.

By contrast, *O. lignaria* belongs to a group of cavity-nesters, the mason and leaf-cutter bees. They belong to the bee family Megachilidae and have three things in common:

1. the females nest primarily in pre-existing cavities such as hollow plant stems or beetle borings in dead wood, though some species do excavate nests in the ground.
2. instead of using a glandular secretion to line and seal cells, they collect substances such as mud, leaf pieces, resin and tiny pebbles or, according to species, even a mixture of two or more of these items.
3. the tract of specialized pollen transporting hairs, the scopa, is situated on the underside of the abdomen.

O. lignaria uses mud as a building material. Other North American species such as the widespread *O. georgica*, use a mastic of finely chewed leaves. *O. lignaria* is widespread and common in much of North America, where it comprises two geographical races or subspecies: *O. lignaria lignaria,* found east of the Rockies and *O. lignaria propinqua,* whose populations are distributed west of the Rockies.

In the wild, the Blue Orchard Mason Bee nests in a wide range of ready-made cavities. It has been recorded from beetle or woodpecker borings in dead wood, deeply fissured bark, hollow plant stems and old nest cells of mud-dauber wasps. Sometimes, it even makes clusters of exposed cells on stones or rock faces. Its natural habitat is open woodland and woodland edge, where there is a good mix of wild flowers and potential nest sites in dead wood.

With their contrived diversity of flowers, gardens are particularly attractive to wild bees. Often, neighborhood gardens have a greater variety of flowers than the surrounding countryside, especially in areas of intensive agriculture. *Osmia lignaria* is no stranger to town gardens and will nest very successfully in cities. The same is true of its Old World relative, *O. rufa,* which, in much of Britain and Europe, is now commoner in town gardens than in farmland.

If your house has overlapping roof tiles or walls clad with wooden shingles, then you may already be host to a nesting population: the spaces between these structures are ideal nesting cavities for this versatile bee.

Sometimes in early spring, females can be seen investigating nail holes in wooden sheds and other structures and, like, *O. rufa,* it sometimes nests in little-used keyholes, discarded lengths of garden cane or ventilation bricks.

The earliest individuals of *O. lignaria* are tempted out by the first really mild days in mid- to late March. It is the males that put in this early appearance. The females emerge a few days later and are active until the end of June to mid-July. The exact dates will vary from year to year and with locality: southern and lowland populations will tend to emerge earlier than those of northern and upland areas.

The Orchard Mason bee is 8-10mm long (1/3 inch), and is covered with dense, black hairs; males are more slender than the females, with longer anten-nae and a tuft of pale hairs on the front of the head. The female's head is larger and squarer than that of the males. This is to accommodate the large muscles associated with the powerful jaws used to excavate mud. Like her European counterpart, *O. rufa,* the female *O. lignaria* has a pair of horns below the anten-nae, hence the alternative popular name for this group of species, the "horn-faced bees." A female uses the horns to tamp mud into position when sealing brood cells and closing a completed nest.

After emergence, the males spend their time feeding on nectar at flowers and flying in an agitated manner around nest entrances, waiting for the females to appear. Males are aggressive towards each other and often jostle for position on some vantage point close to nests. Like all male bees, those of *O. lignaria* do not have a sting.

When the females begin to emerge, there is a mad scramble between the males to be the first to mate. The reason for this extreme competitiveness is that the females usually mate only once and thus males are very quickly confronted with a rapidly diminishing resource in the form of virgin, nubile females. A female needs to mate only once because she stores sperm in a special sac, the **spermatheca,** with a single mating providing more than enough sperm to fertilize her complement of about 40 eggs.

With such a stressful and competitive life-style, the males quickly become ragged and worn, with patches of abraded fur and increasingly frayed wings. They eventually die after about three to four weeks, leaving the females to continue their work of nesting and foraging.

Immediately after emergence, a female *Osmia lignaria* seeks a patch of suitable flowers on which to feed. She needs sugar-rich nectar to fuel all her activities and pollen as a source of protein to complete the maturation of the eggs in her ovaries. Because this is a spring bee and warm weather is not a guaranteed constant, females may frequently become chilled and you can often see them sunning themselves on a leaf or flower or roosting on a warm stone to absorb heat.

During this early period of feeding, a female will have to run the gauntlet of mate-hungry males, who probably detect her presence by scent as well as visual clues; males often patrol feeding areas attractive to females as well as nest sites.

Mating may take place on a leaf, on the ground or, more usually, in the immediate vicinity of nests and the female may occasionally walk around, carrying the male. Throughout, the mating pair is highly attractive to other males, who often pounce on them and try to dislodge the male. I have seen this happen many times in *O. rufa*, but have never seen any male successfully usurp a mating rival.

After mating, both sexes spend time grooming themselves, using legs to smooth down pubescence and clean wings. Eventually, the male takes to the wing and once more is engaged in the pursuit of mates. But for our female, the serious business of nesting now begins.

When she finds a potential nest site, she inspects it carefully by tapping her antennae rapidly around the entrance before entering for more detailed examination. You can follow what a female is doing inside her nest by using a mirror to shine a beam of light into the nest. And this is what you might see: if the prospective nest is an old beetle boring in wood, then she will probably have to clear out remains of old wood fibers and beetle droppings. She will repeatedly back out to the nest entrance, using her abdomen to push debris to the outside. If the nest was in fact used as a nest by a female of the previous season's generation of *O. lignaria,* then you can see her clearing out the remains of left-over pollen, cocoons and the mud partitions between cells.

If our female decides on this particular cavity as her first nest, she may spend some time roosting in it, sitting just inside the entrance. Indeed, by this time, it might be dusk and she will spend the night in her newly chosen home.

As soon as the first sun warms the entrance next morning, our female will begin to stir. She will need to re-fuel on nectar at the nearest suitable flowers, but before she can do this, she must do something that all central place foragers must do: learn her surroundings and memorize cues which will enable her to find her way back to her newly acquired desirable residence.

Like the females of all wasps and bees, our *O. lignaria* has a whole repertoire of behaviors at her disposal which enable her to do just that and in a very precise way.

The first piece of behavior may well be what initially attracts your attention to females nesting in your garden. That is, a female flying repeatedly in a side-to-side, figure-of-eight pattern about what seems to be a central point, namely, her nest entrance. Such a female is memorizing visual landmarks close to her nest, for example, a stone to one side, a clump of flowers next to this, an old plant pot on the other side and a patch of lichen above the nest.

If you watch for long enough, you will see the female widen the sweep of her repetitive figures-of-eight and, at the same time, fly slightly higher and further away. She is now beginning to memorize landmarks that are further away from her nest entrance. She will increase the distance and breadth of her sweeps until she is starting to memorize more distant cues on her horizon. These could include a prominent tree, a church steeple and a far away hill.

Our female will repeat these actions until she has a detailed mental map of her immediate and distant surroundings. She is now ready for that all-too urgent re-fuelling trip and will now set off for a good feed. In so doing, the memorizing still goes on: she remembers other landmarks and the direction from the nest she has flown. This last feat is truly remarkable and just how she does it is a tribute to the efficiency of her tiny brain.

In addition to her ability to construct a mental map of her surroundings, the female bee also memorizes the position of the sun relative to her nest entrance as she flies away from it. Now you might think that the sun is not ideal reference point. After all, it does have the irritating habit of moving across the sky as the day progresses. But our *Osmia* is not in the least fazed by this: she has an on-board clock which enables her to compensate for the sun's movements. And what if clouds obscure the sun? Well, she has another skill at her disposal: her eyes are able to detect the plane of polarized light, so that she knows where the sun is, even if you and I don't and even if there is total cloud cover.

Now our female can feed in earnest *and* find her way back home. Back at the nest, she will make a number of orientation flights, just to fine-tune her memorized landmarks. Now, the business of nesting can begin in earnest.

By now, the female will have a pretty good idea of where the best local nectar and pollen sources are, having spent some time foraging to meet her own immediate needs, but there is one more resource she needs to reconnoiter: mud. She needs a source of preferably fine-grained soil which she can convert into mud of just the right texture for her building requirements. Her first post-feeding foraging trip will be for mud rather than pollen. And this is because her first task is to plaster the rear end of her nest tunnel with a smooth layer of mud.

You may detect females in their search for mud because they fly in a very characteristic pattern: low passes over bare earth, with frequent landings to test the texture of the soil. Sometimes you may see several to many females doing this in the same place because they will all be attracted to the same sort of soil.

Eventually, our female will find just the right spot and start loosening soil with her powerful jaws adding saliva, if necessary, to render it into a malleable paste, behaviour she shares will all the mud using *Osmia* species (Plate 5). Soon the female will have a ball of glistening mud nearly as big as her head. Now she carries this back to her nest and applies it to the rear of the tunnel (Plate 6). She may make two or three mud-gathering trips before she has finished. Having found a suitable area of soil, she will return again and again, throughout her nesting cycle, to what becomes a quarry in miniature. In Europe, several females of *O. rufa* may use the same quarry and may be seen disappearing into the hole they have excavated, behavior which has led to erroneous reports that this bee sometimes nests in the ground.

I discovered one day just how important is a good source of the right textured soil. In 1997, we moved to our present house in Banbury, part of a Victorian terrace with long, narrow back gardens. In the spring of 1998, I ordered two tonnes of topsoil to be delivered. It arrived at 7.30 one Saturday morning and by 9.30am, there was quite a swarm of *O. rufa* females excavating mud and flying off. At that time I had no occupied nests in this garden, my nesting population being housed in a garden elsewhere, so these bees were not "mine."

There were enough bees to form a visible flight line, coming and going from the soil heap, flying down the garden towards the house, then veering upwards and then left, along the roof ridges of the adjacent houses and then diagonally over the roof of a church. I went out to the street and picked up the line of flying bees as they flew diagonally across the street and then over the roofs of the houses about 50m down the street, on the opposite side. At this point I lost them, but this observation demonstrates just how efficient are the females of *O. rufa* in finding a newly created resource, in this case, a two-hour old heap of soil, at least 250m from their nearest possible nest sites.

After smoothing the inner application of mud, the female begins her next task: foraging for pollen. She will visit a wide range of flowers and quickly learns which are the most abundant sources of pollen and nectar at any particular time. When fruit trees such plum, apple, pear and cherry are in full flower, she will major on these for pollen, sometimes visiting other plants for nectar.

When she visits, say, an apple tree, she will land on a flower and scrabble for pollen, using her legs to loosen it from the anthers. Soon she becomes dusted with the yellow powder and begins to compact it in the dense brush of hairs forming the scopa on the underside of her abdomen. However, she is not as efficient as the honeybee in grooming herself and plenty of pollen remains on all areas of her body. And this is what makes her such an ideal pollinator: her less than perfect grooming means that pollen is easily dislodged on to the receptive stigma when she visits the flowers of another tree.

It takes between 8-15 foraging trips to gather enough pollen to provision a cell. You can tell how many pollen loads a cell has because if you open up a completed one, before the egg has hatched and the larva has started feeding, you can see the different layers of pollen, each one representing a single foraging trip. If your female has visited different plants on successive trips, you can often see pollen layers of different color. Every now and then, the female adds a little nectar to the pollen mass.

The reason for the variation in the numbers of foraging trips is to do with the sex of her offspring: female bees are larger and their larvae need more food, while the more slender males need less pollen. Sometimes, a female makes a mistake and lays a male egg in a female cell and a giant male is the result the following spring; and the opposite happens if, by mistake, a female lays a female egg in a male cell: a dwarf daughter is the result.

The deeper cells in the nest almost always contain females while the outermost cells are almost always male.

When our female has fully provisioned her first cell, she lays a single, pearly white egg on top of the pollen (Plate 7). She then gathers enough mud to build a wall which seals the cell. She repeats the process until she has provisioned a row of cells, each with a single egg and partitioned from its neighbor by a mud wall. The final cell to be completed is always about 1-2cm from the nest entrance. She then seals the nest with mud, leaving an empty, vestibular cell between the nest closure and the first cell. This is believed to be a deterrent to certain parasites which lay their eggs in *Osmia* nests (see below).

After completing her first nest, the female will start another one in a nearby tube. In her short adult life of 10-12 weeks, she might make a total of four to five nests. Meanwhile, the eggs in her first nest will eventually hatch and the larvae feed voraciously on the stored pollen (Plate 8).

The female's life's work involves a complex sequence of stereotyped behaviors:-

nest searching → nest inspection → mud gathering → mud application → pollen gathering→ egg laying → mud gathering → mud application → pollen gathering and so on. Here, the completion of one task is the stimulus to begin the next task in the sequence.

I never cease to be impressed by the skills of these and other nesting wasps and bees. Consider the processing power that makes the nesting cycle possible, together with the homing abilities described above and all this is accomplished with an on-board computer about the size of a grain of sugar!

All the while she has been nesting, our female has not been alone: although a solitary species, *O. lignaria* likes to nest gregariously and several females may use a nest kit simultaneously.

As a typical solitary bee, a female *O. lignaria* does not live to see her offspring. Towards the end of June, the females are getting worn and tattered: then a female's fur may have been bleached gray by the sun and the middle of her thorax and abdomen may well be bald because of constant abrasion against the nest walls. And the ends of her wings will be badly frayed.

Very old females can often be seen sitting at the nest entrances, usually showing a distinct tremor and it is now that some very old females may show distinct signs of senile behavior: a female may provision and seal cells without laying an egg, or, more often, simply partition completely empty cells. Perhaps this behavior indicates that she has run out of eggs.

A fine tremor, though, isn't always a signal of senility. I was once observing the behavior of a nesting population in England of the Red Mason Bee, *Osmia rufa* and my attention was drawn to a larger than usual female because she was stealing fresh mud from the nests of neighboring females.

This female left on a foraging trip and was away for rather longer than usual. When she returned with what seemed like an incomplete pollen load, she sat at her nest entrance for some time before entering. She had a fine tremor affecting her whole body. Eventually, she entered head first, then reappeared at the entrance and backed in to deposit her pollen. Then she left and flew very slowly to a spot close by, where she and other females had been gathering mud. Here she walked about, still trembling noticeably and gathered a rather small load of mud. I followed her back to the nest, where she sat trembling at the entrance and deposited the mud. She made no attempt to manipulate the mud any further, but simply sat there, trembling.

I decided to look at her more closely under the microscope and see if I could find out what was the matter with her. My intention was to kill her humanely and look inside her abdomen to see if some internal parasite might be the cause of her tremor and slow, awkward movements. However, as soon as I got her under the microscope, I saw what was the matter. There was crack in her head capsule that ran from the top of the head, down along the inner margin of her right eye and across the front of the face. The bee had obviously flown into a plate glass window or had been hit by a car to cause such an injury. The fact that she carried on with nest provisioning and mud gathering, though with growing difficulty, testifies to the strength of the instinctive urge to nest and reproduce.

Eventually, the females die but already their offspring are active: the eggs will have hatched into tiny larvae which begin to feed voraciously on the stored pollen. Initially, their soft cuticle can expand as they increase in size, but eventually, they have to moult their skins. During the feeding and developmental period, each larva moults 4-5 times (Plate 8). When the larva is fully grown, there is little or no pollen left. Eventually, round about mid-August to the beginning of September, the larva spins a tough brown cocoon and enters the pupal stage. During this period, larval tissues are broken down and reassembled to form the adult bee.

The bees become adult in September and remain inside their cocoons until the following spring, when they emerge and begin the cycle anew.

Nest associates
Nesting birds have a number of hangers on, species such as dermestid beetles (sometimes called carpet beetles), which feed on feather and skin debris which accumulate at the bottom of the nest.

Nesting bees also have their associates and *Osmia lignaria* is no exception; their nests are host to a species of mite called *Chaetodactylus krombeini,* named after the eminent Smithsonian entomologist, Dr. K. V. Krombein, whose pioneering studies of nesting wasps and bees paved the way for the use of artificial nests for bees.

Mites are minute relatives of spiders. They enter the nest cells when the female bee is away on a foraging trip. They feed on uneaten pollen left by larvae. In this capacity they are best regarded as associates acting as scavengers. But when present in large numbers, they reportedly eat the bee egg and consume the pollen and breed and multiply within the pollen mass. In the following spring, any adult bees which emerge from behind a mite infested cell bite their way through it on their out and, in so doing, pick up hundreds or even thousands of the tiny mites which cover their entire bodies.

When the bee first visits a flower many of the mites jump off and remain to infest another *Osmia* when in visits and get transported back to her nest. In Europe, nests of the Red Mason Bee, *Osmia rufa,* host a related mite species, *Chaetodactylis osmiae.* This mite is most numerous in cells in which the egg or young larva has died, but seems to live quite amicably alongside feeding bee larvae, eating pollen grains adhering to the sides of the cell and out of reach of the larvae. As with *Chaetodactlyis krombeini,* I believe that this mite is mostly a nest scavenger rather than a parasite of the bee.

With *Osmia rufa,* I have noticed that if male bees are infested with mites, they eventually congregate at the end of his abdomen, close to the genitalia. Indeed, when, in the course of research I had to dissect the genitalia of males, I often found that the genital cavity was packed with mites. I surmised that this was to facilitate the venereal transmission of the mites and, sure enough, when I once found a mating pair in which the male was heavily infested, I was able to see, with the aid of a magnifying glass, the mites leaving the male to climb on to the female's body. She was then primed to infect her nest when she started one.

Enemies

Like all animals and plants, *Osmia lignaria* has natural enemies. Some are generalist predators such as birds and spiders, but other are much more specialized and adapted to prey specifically on *O. lignaria* and its close bee relatives.

Those sometimes found attacking *Osmia lignaria* include beetles and parasitic wasps and a fungus. The commonest beetle parasite is called *Tricrania stansburyi*. This belongs to a group of beetles often called oil or blister beetles. It is black, with deep red wing cases.

After mating, a female *Tricrania* flies to a plant, where it lays a clutch of up to 400 eggs. These hatch after about a week into very peculiar and specialized larvae called triungulins. Each is tiny, but very agile and rather heavily armor plated, with a pair of long spines at the rear end of the body. They climb up the plant and into the flower. Here they wait for the next foraging bee: using the prominent claws on their feet, they grasp hold of the bee's hairs and climb aboard, gripping on to a hair with their well-developed jaws. In this way, they hitch a ride back to the bee's nest, there to wreak havoc. If more than one triungulin arrives at the nest, there is a fight to the death, with the sole survivor then sinking its jaws into the bee's egg and eating its contents. The beetle larva then completes its development, feeding on the stored pollen. After pupating and becoming adult, the beetle remains inside the bee nest until the following spring, when it emerges, mates and starts the cycle all over again. *Tricrania stansburyi* is known to parasitize at least ten other bee species in North America. With the exception of the mining bee *Anthophora edwardsi*, all of these other hosts are cavity-nesting mason bees related to *Osmia,* including *O. cornifrons,* a species introduced from Japan for apple pollination.

Another beetle nest associate is the carpet beetle, *Anthrenus verbasci.* This is not a specialized parasite or predator of mason bees. It is sometimes called the Carpet Beetle because its densely hairy larvae often cause damage by eating woollen carpets. This habit reflects the fact that the larvae are associated with mammal and bird nests, where they scavenge on skin or feather debris.

Although this beetle is widespread and common in Europe, in 30 years of rearing the Red Mason Bee, *Osmia rufa,* I have never found it in my nests and I know of no recorded instance of any association with bee nests in the Old World. However, as a museum worker, I am all too well aware of its other common name, the Museum Beetle, for the versatile larvae of this beetle are pests of insect collections, bird and mammal skins and all natural history museums wage a constant battle against them.

Given the generalist feeding habits of the larvae of *Anthrenus verbasci,* it is obvious that female beetles are attracted to old nests of *Osmia lignaria* by the presence of either adult bees which have died in their natal cocoons or dry pollen stores in cells where eggs have failed to hatch or larvae have died.

The wasp enemies of *Osmia lignaria* are various: at least five species have been recorded. One of them is a tiny, metallic green chalcid wasp, about 2mm long, called *Monodontomerus obscurus.* This species only attacks long after the cell is completed, sealed and the bee larva has spun a cocoon and has pupated or is about to. The female wasp has an egg-laying tube or **ovipositor** protruding from the end of her abdomen and she uses this to inject eggs through the side of a plant stem into an *Osmia* cell and through the silk cocoon and on to the mature bee larva or pupa. The eggs hatch out and the larvae feed as parasites on the developing bee, eventually killing it.

Monodontomerus obscurus has been recorded from two other North American bees, *Osmia cordata* and the leaf cutter bee, *Megachile rotundata.* The wasp is also found in Europe, where it parasitizes the Red Mason Bee, *Osmia rufa,* a fact which underlines just how closely related these two mason bees are to one another. A single pupa of *Osmia rufa* will support the development of 15-20 of these tiny wasps (Plate 9); I suspect that the smaller *O. lignaria* would support rather fewer.

The design of the nester tubes described below protects your bees from this enemy: the combination of tough cardboard guard tube and inner liner make it impossible for the *Monodontomerus* female to penetrate the cell with her ovipositor.

Another wasp parasite of *Osmia lignaria* is much larger, about 10-12mm long. It is called *Sapyga angustata* and a female enters a cell while the bee is away foraging. She lays one or two eggs, sometimes directly on to the host egg and these hatch before that of the bee. The first thing they do is to suck out the contents of the bee egg before going on to complete their development feeding on the stored pollen.

One enemy of *Osmia lignaria* comes from a little closer to home: it is itself a bee, more precisely, a cuckoo bee. This is *Stelis montana,* which, as the "cuckoo" appellation implies, lays its eggs in the nests of other bees: a female cuckoo bee patrols the *Osmia* nest site and waits until a female leaves on a foraging trip. While the rightful owner is away, the *Stelis* female enters the nest and lays an egg in the stored pollen. Her egg will eventually hatch and the cuckoo larva kills the host larva and then eats the pollen.

The fungus which sometimes attacks *O. lignaria* has also been recorded from the honeybee. It is called *Ascophaera torchioi* and infections cause a condition called chalkbrood: when the larvae eat they take in fungal spores with their food, the spores germinate and fungal threads spread throughout the larva's body, eventually killing it.

THREE

Using nester kits for the Blue Orchard Mason bee

Background to the nest design

A nester kit comprises an outer plastic cylinder containing cardboard nest tubes, each of which contains a removable paper liner (Plate 14). The liner is held in place at the rear of the tube by a plastic stopper which also acts as a grip when removing the liner. The lined tubes were devised by Dr. Phil Torchio, formerly of the USDA Bee Systematics and Biology Lab at Logan, Utah.

The advantage of the liner is that is that one can remove it at the end of the season and hold it up against a strong light and examine the nest for cells which contain bees killed by disease or parasites. The dead cells can be removed and whole, healthy cocoons transferred to a fresh tube.

The combination of thick, outer cardboard tube and inner liner provides protection against one of the worst enemies of *Osmia lignaria,* a tiny chalcidoid wasp, *Monodontomerus obscurus* (See Section 2 above on enemies).

The nest kits mimic two of the commonest natural nest sites of *Osmia lignaria,* hollow plant stems and beetle borings in dead wood. There are three reasons why they are so effective as nests and they all center on time, that all-important resource for a bee that is active for a relatively short period in a season where the weather can be unpredictable:-

1. each kit provides a concentrated array of nests in a single place, so nest-seeking females at the beginning of the season are saved much time because once they have found a nest kit, and completed their first nests, they do not have to search again for another suitable nest cavity.

2. with the nesters, a female does not have to spend time cleaning out the usual debris – beetle droppings, wood fibers, pith, etc – which are to be found in natural nest sites (although if she is using a tube in a nest kit used the previous season, she *will* have to invest time in some cleaning work, but the smooth nest interior makes this a much easier task.)

3. with nesters, the constant internal dimensions require minimal amounts of mud for cell partitions and nest closure. By contrast, irregularly shaped cavities such as the normal nest sites and places such as cavities in stones, between shingles, deep cracks in bark, require much more mud to reduce spaces down to normal cell size and, consequently, a larger investment in time and energy in gathering extra mud.

Propagation

i. In gardens and backyard plots

Many urban and suburban areas in North America have wild populations of the Blue Orchard Mason Bee, *Osmia lignaria*. Because their nest sites tend to be scattered, the bees are easily overlooked and you may have a healthy population in your neighborhood without realizing it.

A completely wind-sheltered east or south-facing spot which catches the morning sun is ideal. Failing that, the best places to site your nest are sheltered, sunny spots facing south or south east Avoid north-facing situations at all costs.

Ensure that overhanging or trailing vegetation does not obscure your nests. You may think that you are helping the bees (and your fruit set!) by placing the nests as close as possible to fruit trees, but the bees do not like dappled shade or nests which are moved by wind, so it is not normally a good idea to not attach nests directly to trees: the bees are quite capable of finding your fruit blossoms and any other flowers you want them to visit. However, if you have mature trees and can secure nests against being moved by the wind and you can be sure they will get direct sunlight, then fixing them directly to trees is alright.

It is also important to make sure that the nests are well above ground to avoid splashing with soil during heavy rain.

So, where are the best places to put your nests? More than 30 years of experience with *Osmia rufa* has taught me that placing nests on isolated wooden or metal stakes in the middle of a garden is *not* very successful in terms of high rates of occupation and the same is true for *O. lignaria*. My greatest success has been with nests placed on walls which are at least 75cm (29-30in) high or attached to wooden fence posts. Other suitable nest sites include the eaves of garden sheds and garages, especially if they are made of wood or, among log piles. Log piles are particularly attractive because females are attracted to them in search of beetle borings and emergence holes.

Osmia lignaria often nests in between roof tiles and in the spaces between wall shingles. If you have a nesting population in such sites, then you can get the bees to use your nesters by placing them close by. A good proportion of nest-seeking females will find your nests and establish themselves there.

All of these situations are in marginal positions, at the edge of things, and I think the reason for their success is that the richest source of natural nest sites are woodland edge, where dead tree stumps and branches are both likely to occur in sunny situations. Here beetles will bore into the timber, providing future nest sites for bees. In other words, the bees are programmed to search along woodland edges and the margins of clearings. For this reason, if you are unsure if there is a nesting population in your area, it is a good idea to put some nesters out in some woodland edge. Keep an eye on them and any occupied nests can be brought to your garden in late summer for overwintering.

Apart from providing nest sites for your bees, you can help them by planting flowers and shrubs they are particularly fond of. If you have a good mix of fruit trees, raspberries and early flowering strawberries, then you are in business. The mix of species described in Section 5 is excellent but I would single out the geraniums and wallflowers, especially Siberian Wallflower and the shrub *Pieris japonica*.

When your nests have attracted bees, their nesting activities will be very obvious and you can have hours of fun watching them. A mud seal indicates a completed nest. In a good season you may get nearly 100 percent occupancy of your nest tubes. If you wish to expand in the following season, you can always obtain addition nest kits from (KINSMAN COMPANY INC., 6805 EASTON ROAD, P.O. BOX 428, PIPERSVILLE, PA 18947, TELEPHONE (215) 766-5613, FAX (215) 766-5600.)

If you decide to have more than one nest kit, then it is a good idea to locate them in two's in different locations about the garden, rather than concentrate them all in the same place. But do remember the general rules about aspect and positioning.

ii. In orchards

USDA scientists at the Bee Systematics and Biology Lab at Logan, Utah and the USDA Lab at Beltsville, Maryland, are the world's leading experts in the use of solitary bees as managed pollinators. The pioneering studies by Dr Phil Torchio in the west and Dr. Suzanne Batra in the east have built up a huge body of knowledge on the life histories of these bees and how to manage them. Moreover, their painstaking research has demonstrated just how efficient solitary bees are as pollinators, especially of fruit trees: apples, pears, plums, and almonds and how, in some circumstances, mason bees are more effective pollinators than honeybees.

For the positioning of nesters in orchards, the same considerations apply as in gardens: do not place nests in fruit trees unless tree trunks are sufficiently sturdy not to move in the wind and they receive direct sunlight. Instead, place them in raised situations at the edge of your plot. Wooden shelters raised well off the ground are ideal. It is a good idea to stretch chicken wire over the entrance to the shelter: this does not impede the bees, but protects against woodpeckers, which sometime peck at nest tubes and damage them.

Patches of bare earth may not be a feature of your orchard, so it is a good idea to create some around your plot to provide the bees with a ready source of building materials; sheltered, shady spots are best. Alternatively, you can distribute seed trays around the orchard with crumbly, aerated soil. If this gets too dry, add just a little water – a momentary spray from a watering can will be sufficient.

The nesters should be evenly distributed around your orchard's margins. As a rule of thumb, about 250 females of *Osmia lignaria* will adequately pollinate 1 acre of apples at commercial densities (= 620 females per hectare). This contrasts favorably with the honeybee, where on average, the literature recommends 3 honeybee colonies per hectare of apples, each with a minimum number of 20,000 active workers. Thus if 620 females of *O. lignaria* will do the pollinating work of 60,000 honeybees, then, one female is the pollinating equivalent of 96 honeybee workers.

In practice, it is difficult to have built up honeybee populations to such sizes so early in the year and more hives may have to be introduced to compensate. With apple and other rosaceous fruit crops, honeybees have a tendency to land directly on the petals and minimize their direct contact with the pollen-bearing anthers and will often probe the flowers from the side to gain access to the nectaries without coming into contact with pollen. This is particularly prevalent with the "Golden Delicious" variety of apples, one of the most commercially important crops.

By contrast, *Osmia* females come into direct contact with the sexual parts of the flower and are principally interested in handling pollen. All in all, then, *Osmia lignaria* is a more efficient pollinator of orchard crops than the honeybee and there is great potential for its further commercial development.

Recently, USDA scientists in Utah showed that this remarkable bee is an excellent pollinator of sweet cherries, producing very exciting results: not only was yield improved by nearly 270 per cent, there was also a gratifying and demonstrable improvement in quality, so much so that 94 per cent of the crop made the "perfect grade" and they were the best cherries the local fruit inspector had seen that season.

iii.Overwintering: garden and orchard reared bees

Leave your occupied nests in position until late September or early October. Up until then, your bees are a little vulnerable and, if moved too soon, there may be some mortality. But in early autumn you have to decide how you want to overwinter your bees.

Before so doing, you can if you want, eliminate diseased or parasitized cells: simply use a razor blade to slit open the inner nest liners and remove healthy cocoons. If a mud partitioned cell does not contain a brown silk oval cocoon, then something went wrong: There may be a mass of yellow, often moldy pollen, indicating that the egg or young larva died before finishing its food; the cell may contain a chalky, mummified bee larva, in which case you have a chalk brood infection. If so, it is a good idea to destroy the nest tube and all contents, including healthy cocoons to minimize the possibility of infecting next year's generation.

Take your healthy cocoons and place them in a new liner and in the same order they were arranged in their original nest. It is important to ensure that the head end of the cocoon faces what you decide to be the front of the nest. The head end is easy to recognize: it has a cap or nipple in which the silk is less dense and paler than the rest of the cocoon; the rear of the cocoon is uniform in color and texture. You then have two choices:-

1. Place a nester or box containing occupied tubes in an unheated shed or garage. The latter should not be attached to the house because then it will be too warm. In early spring, place the liners back into the outer guard tubes. If you are re-using guard tubes from the previous season, it is a good idea to use the rear, unweathered end of the guard tube as the front. Then use your judgment as to when to place the nests back in their spot in the garden, allotment or orchard. The beginning of March is usually a good time, but take into consideration local weather conditions: is it a mild spring, or is the season a bit late? In northern areas it might be a good idea to delay placing the nests by about 10 days.

2. Place your occupied nests in a cardboard box insulated with crumpled newspaper and keep it in the refrigerator over winter at 38°F (3-4°C). The bees will cope with this quite well and the low temperatures may kill any parasites you may have missed. By refrigerating the bees, you can delay their emergence if the spring is late. In such circumstances, keep an eye on the weather and check with the long range weather forecasts. About 14 days before you think the fine weather will begin, remove then from the refrigerator and keep them at room temperature, for about a week; then replace them in backyard or garden.

FOUR

Frequently asked questions

Q1   How can I be sure that Blue Orchard Mason bees will find and use my nests?

A1   The females of *Osmia lignaria* are very adept at finding suitable nest sites. If you have followed the instructions which came with the nest kit, they will find them. When you think of their natural nest sites, hollow plant stems and beetle borings in dead wood, these are not evenly distributed in the environment, especially in the garden situation. Thus, nest-seeking females in spring *have simply got* to be good at finding a scarce resource. By putting out nester kits, you are making life much easier for the bees. An apartment block of this sort is bee heaven! You have saved them the time and effort that would have been involved in clearing out beetle and earwig droppings from borings and plant stems.

Once a female has started to use your nest kit, others will soon follow: they seem to be attracted to the activities of other females.

Q2   Will the offspring of my bees use my nests the following season?

A2   Yes and no. While females have strong tendency to nest close to where they emerged, perhaps as many as 50 percent of your newly emerged females will disperse and nest somewhere else. This loss will be offset to some extent by the nest-seeking females from elsewhere which wander into your backyard. Also, being gregarious little bees, the nesting activities of resident females attract other females to your nests. Bees will re-use old nest tubes after clearing out the remains of the previous season's nest activity: old cell partitions, remains of pollen stores and cocoons. **However,** after two or three years, the ends of the nest tubes close to the entrance may become weathered and need replacing. You can order replacements and additional nest kits from (KINSMAN COMPANY INC., 6805 EASTON ROAD, P.O. BOX 428, PIPERSVILLE, PA 18947, TELEPHONE (215) 766-5613, FAX (215) 766-5600.]. It is, in any case, a good idea to replace nester tubes after two season to minimize the build up of disease organisms such as the chalkbrood fungus (See Enemies section, above)

You can improve the chances of your bees' survival by overwintering them as described in the nest kit instructions or on page xx of this book.

Q3   The bee developing at the back of the nest is from the first egg to be laid and is therefore the oldest, so doesn't it wake up first in spring and

don't the younger bees in front trap it?

A3   This is the most frequently asked question and the answer is: Yes and no! And I found out the answer when helping to make a television program about solitary bees. We took a block of wood in which *Osmia rufa* had nested in specially drilled tunnels in the previous season and sectioned one of the nests. The exposed section was covered with a piece of clear plastic so that emergence of the bees in spring could be filmed and, sure enough, we saw the answer to the question acted out in front of us. True to prediction, the oldest bee, that is, the one in the first and therefore deepest cell, woke up from winter hibernation first, but this happened in two stages. In *Osmia rufa* and *O. lignaria* and other tube-nesting mason bees, cells containing females tend to be at the rear of the nest, with males at the front and males tend to emerge several days before the females.

So, it was the innermost (and thus oldest) male which woke up first. Using his jaws, he bit his way through the tough silk cocoon he had spun as a full-grown larva and then chewed through the mud partition separating his cell from that of the bee in front. He then bit into the cocoon of the bee in front of him and nipped its backside. This woke the second bee up and he in turn chewed through the front of his cocoon and through the mud partition into the cell in front of him. And he too nipped the backside of the bee in front of *him*. In this way, a chain reaction was established and in the course of half a day, all the male bees in the nest tunnel were awakened and ready to start to leave the nest. A few days later, the same thing happened with the females, with the innermost initiating activity until all the female bees were active and ready to leave the nest and start the cycle anew: mating, nesting, pollen and mud gathering and egg-laying. There is no doubt that the same waking up sequence occurs with *O. lignaria* as well.

Q4   What can I do if I have mason bees nesting in my walls or in air-bricks or between roof tiles?

A4   Don't worry! You can stage a rescue operation using nester kits. In late March-early April, just before the bees should start nesting, place a nester kit (or kits) close to where the bees are nesting inappropriately. When the females emerge and start looking for nest sites, they will preferentially choose the nice clean nests you have so kindly provided. The reason for this is simple: were they to re-use the irregular cavities in the wall or spaces between roof tiles, the females would have to spend a lot of time and energy clearing out the debris from the previous year's nesting activities; by moving into your nice new apartment block, they are saved this labor. And, in the unpredictable weather of early spring, if time is not exactly money for these bees, it certainly has a value which can be translated into that most vital of resources: pollen!

Q5   Why are Mason bees safe with children and pets?

A5   It is true that like almost all female bees, *Osmia* females each have a sting. However, they are not in the least bit aggressive. And the reason for this is simple: they are solitary bees and, unlike the highly social honeybee, do not store large amounts of honey, so they do not have a large and valuable resource to protect.

I have worked with the European *O. rufa* for 30 years and handled females many times without being stung. For example, this has involved pushing females to one side while using a mirror to direct a beam of light into a nest to observe a female's activities while in her nest. In these circumstances, females have never responded aggressively. When, however, I knew that I would be encouraging people to keep these bees in their gardens, I thought I ought to find out just how much provocation was needed to induce a female to sting. I therefore took a female and rolled her between my fingers. Eventually she stung me and this was a mere pinprick, with none of the long-term pain and swelling one associates with stings from honeybees, bumblebees and social wasps. Indeed, the sensory experience was all over in a couple of minutes.

The lesson here is simple and obvious: unless you handle a female *Osmia* very roughly with your fingers, you are simply not going to get stung. This means it is quite safe for you and your children to observe these fascinating bees as closely as you please. And there is nothing at all to fear from the smaller males: like the males of all bees and wasps, they simply have no sting.

Q6   What other solitary bees can I expect to use my nests?

A6   Apart from the Blue Orchard Bee, *Osmia lignaria,* you can expect, depending on where you live, several other species of mason bee to use the nesters described in this book. These include *Osmia georgica* and *O. coerulescens.* Both of these species use a mastic of chewed leaves rather than mud as a building material and really prefer narrower nest tubes than those intended for *O. lignaria. O. coerulescens* is found in certain Rocky Mountain areas in the west and a number of central and eastern states and is active from June to the end of July; it is a native of Europe and North Africa and is believed to have been accidentally introduced to the United States.   Another introduced species is *O. cornifrons,* whose natural distribution is China, Japan and Korea (Plate 3). This was imported from Japan by USDA scientists to evaluate its potential as a managed pollinator of apples and is established in parts of Utah and in some eastern states.

In addition to the Blue Orchard Mason Bee, there are more than 130 species of *Osmia* in North America, though not all of them will use your nests.

As well as mason bees, your nesters may also attract several species of leafcutter bees, *Megachile* spp. In England, two species of *Megachile* use the nesters which I put for *Osmia rufa*. They do not much like the paper liners: before using a nest tube, a female will bite out a section of the liner and drop it on the ground. She repeats the process until nearly all of the liner has been removed. I know of no reports of female leafcutter bees doing this in North America with this type of paper lined nest.

Q7   If, by providing nests for the Blue Orchard Mason Bee, I build up populations to large levels, will I threaten other pollinators such as bumblebees and honeybees in my garden and those of my neighbors?

A7   No and for a number of reasons:

- *Osmia lignaria* is active for no more than 10-12 weeks in the year, whereas the social bumblebees and honeybee are active for 8-9 months.

- *O. lignaria* is active in spring, when bumblebee colonies have not yet built up the colonies to full size and so competitive interactions are minimal.

- while there is some overlap between bumblebees and *O. lignaria* in terms of the flowers they visit, bumblebees have much longer tongues than those of mason bees and tend to visit flowers with deeper corolla tubes, so this is another way in which competition is avoided.

- bumblebees and honeybees need to collect and store large amounts of nectar in the form of honey, whereas *O. lignaria* and all the other mason bees stores only pollen, slightly moistened with a very little nectar. Thus, the social bees are largely nectar driven while the solitary bees, including *O. lignaria,* are largely pollen driven. True, the social bees *do* gather pollen, but at any one time, not all the work force is engaged in this activity.

- many of the smaller solitary mining bees are mainly active towards the end of *O. lignaria's* nesting period, with their peak of activity in mid-late summer.

In England whenever, I have had *O. rufa* nests, I have never noted any deterioration in the abundance of other bees. In one garden of mine in Oxford, I recorded a total of 54 bee species, while my present garden in Banbury boasts 35 species. Gardeners in the United States and southern Canada can expect many more species than this because the North American bee fauna has many more species than Britain and western Europe.

FIVE

The need to conserve our wild bees and what you can do

Modern intensive agriculture has produced a landscape which is no longer very bee-friendly. There are real economies of scale in growing very large stands of crops, especially oil-seed rape and cereals such as wheat and corn, with little or no "wasted" marginal land where wild flowers may grow and which would harbor nests sites for both cavity nesting bees and mining bees.

Another cause of decline in our bees has been the loss of old, traditional hay meadows. With most cattle now being fed on silage, there has been little call for old-style hay making in recent years. The mowing regime used to manage hay meadows maintained a high diversity of wild flowers which were a valuable forage resource for the native bee fauna. In Britain, the reduced floral diversity and loss of nesting habitats associated with intensive agriculture has had a dire effect on the native bees: 25 per cent of species are now listed in *The Red Data Book* as endangered. The figures are somewhat worse for parts of central Europe and the general decline in the abundance and diversity of wild bees is a serious issue.

In North America, while areas of intensive agriculture have seen local declines in wild bee populations, a much greater proportion of the landscape is closer to natural habitats than in Britain and Europe and, continentally speaking, things are not nearly as bad for native bee faunas as they are in Britain and parts of Europe. However, the pressure is on, especially from over-fragmentation of habitat and people in North America can take steps now to ensure that things never get as bad as they are in Europe.

It is important to be aware of the dangers inherent in losing native bees to intensive agriculture: it is from within their ranks that we will have to recruit alternatives to the honeybee as managed crop pollinators, especially of fruit. This is because apiculture has been in decline because of the devastation caused by the *Varroa* mite. Control measures for this parasite have made bee-keeping a more expensive and labor intensive activity; in the last 10 years, 40-45% of bee-keepers in the UK have given up and there has been a similar decline across Europe and much of the United States.

What you can do: planning a bee-friendly garden
As well as providing bees with nests, which is the main subject of this book, the simplest thing you can do to help native bees is to grow flowers which they par-

ticularly like. A variety of traditional garden flowers is fine, including plants such as cranesbills and geraniums (*Geranium* spp.), wallflowers (*Cheiranthus* spp. and cultivars, especially Siberian Wallflower), stonecrops (*Sedum* spp.,) deadnettles (*Lamium* spp.), sages (*Salvia* spp.), lavenders (*Lavendula* spp), Lamb's Ears (*Stachys lanata*), Custard and Cream (*Limnanthes douglasii*), Comfreys (*Symphytum* spp.), Hound's Tongue (*Cynoglossum officinale*), Bugloss (*Anchusa* and *Echium* spp.), Alkanet (*Alkanna* spp.), Borage (*Borago officinalis*), mignonettes (*Reseda* spp.), Feverfew (*Tanacetum vulgare*).

All of the aromatic culinary herbs are valuable forage for bees and include thymes (*Thymus* spp.), oregano (*Origanum* spp.), Horehound *(Marrubium vulgare)*. And many gardening supply centers and hardware stores now sell seed mixtures of native flowers.

In planning your bee-friendly garden, try to avoid double-flowered varieties. These monstrosities are a tribute to plant-breeders' ingenuity rather than anyone's wisdom: they are of no use to bees simply because the sexual parts of the flower such as the pollen-producing anthers and the female stigma have been replaced by whorls of extra petals and many have lost the ability to produce nectar.

SIX

Other solitary bees managed for pollination: the on-going search

Research in Europe has shown that *Osmia rufa* is a highly efficient pollinator, especially of fruit crops. Yet we are only just beginning to exploit this useful insect. In this we are far behind the United States, Canada and Japan, where several solitary bees are managed very successful as crop pollinators.

In North America and Canada, the best-known and most successful solitary bee exploited by farmers is the Alfalfa Leafcutter bee *Megachile rotundata* (Plate 10) . Alfalfa (*Medicgao sativa*) is an important forage crop for cattle. Like all members of the pea family, its flower has a spring-loaded release mechanism: when a bee probes the flower for nectar, its body weight on the lower "keel" petals trips the mechanism and the anther-bearing stamens spring out and dust the underside of the bee with pollen.

Honeybees do not like this sudden tripping mechanism and avoid it by entering the side of the flower and therefore rarely effect pollination. Thus, when alfalfa was assuming importance as a forage crop in the USA and Canada, the hunt was on for an alternative to the honeybee as a managed pollinator.

The wild ancestor of cultivated alfalfa is not a native of North America: it originates in the Mediterranean region and the steppes and semi-deserts of Asia. By a stroke of pure good fortune, one of its native pollinators in the Old World, a tiny leaf-cutter bee, was accidentally introduced into North America and was discovered there sometime in the 1930's. Just exactly how this tiny bee crossed the Atlantic is unclear, but it almost certainly got there because of its nesting habits: like *Osmia lignaria,, Megachile rotundata* is a typical cavity nesting bee and nests in hollow plant stems and beetle borings in dead wood. Timber or plant material containing occupied nests was almost certainly imported into North America, maybe as packing material and thus human agency facilitated the migration of this bee to the New World.

In parts of Canada and the western United States, the rearing of this little bee for the pollination of alfalfa is now big business. And if you drive through parts of California and Utah, you will see large trailers parked in alfalfa fields, each containing thousands of nests of *Megachile rotundata* made in wooden boards drilled for the purpose (Plate 11). The alfalfa growers hire the bee-trailers each year from firms which specialize in propagating the bee. When alfalfa flowering is over, the completed bee nests in their trailers are towed away, carefully overwintered and then hired out the following season.

There is another solitary bee which has been managed for alfalfa pollina-tion, the Alkali Bee, *Nomia melanderi.* Unlike the Alfalfa Leafcutter Bee, this species is native to North America. It is a mining bee and is called the Alkali Bee because it likes to nest in dense aggregations in salt flats in the western United States. It is possible to construct earth banks around the margins of alfalfa fields with just the right soil texture and salt content to mimic its natural nest site, but it is difficult to maintain the right levels of soil moisture and it is much easier and cheaper to use the leaf-cutter bee, so the alkali bee is no longer used.

Mason bees have been introduced into the United Sates from Japan (*Osmia cornifrons*) (Plate 3) and Spain (*O. cornuta*) for the pollination of orchard fruits. In Japan, *O. cornifrons* is managed commercially as a pollinator of apple crops and *O. cornuta* has been used for almond pollination in California. The commercial exploitation of these imported bees is not yet developed and perhaps it never will be: *O. lignaria,* has been shown to be a very efficient pollinator of several fruit crops, including almonds, apples and cherries.

This species is widespread and common over much of North America and takes readily to the sort of nest kits described here. Although not yet managed on a large scale for commercial pollination, it has great potential and in parts of the western United States gardeners can purchase both nests and bees and the keeping of this docile bee is a growing hobby.

Another native species, *O. ribifloris* (Plate 12), has been shown to be an ef-fective pollinator of highbush blueberry, *Vaccinium australe*, in California and at least three other native American species of *Osmia* have potential as managed pollinators.

It is clear that the wild bee faunas of our planet are an important natural resource, well worth studying and conserving, not least because every third mouthful of human food is dependent either directly or indirectly on the pollina-tion services of bees. Moreover, it is not just for food that we depend on bees: much of the visual impact of landscapes we value for aesthetic reasons is the result of the network of mutually dependent relationships between bees and flow-ering plants.

SEVEN

Where to get your bee nester kits

Nester kits are available in two sizes: 32 and 105 tube nest canisters (Plate 13). Both come with a complete set of instructions. Replacement nest tubes are available separately as are paper liners.

For a price list and to order nest kits, contact: KINSMAN COMPANY INC., 6805 EASTON ROAD, P.O. BOX 428, PIPERSVILLE, PA 18947, TELE-PHONE (215) 766-5613, FAX (215) 766-5600.

Nest kits described in this book originate with Oxford Bee Company Ltd., which is a spinout company of Oxford University. Website www.oxbeeco.com

Further Reading

Trap-Nesting Wasps and Bees: Life Histories Nests and Associates,
by Karl V. Krombein, Smithsonia Press, Washington, D.C., 570pp, 1967.
[The first ever detailed survey of the nesting biologies of cavity-nesting wasps and bees in North America.]

Bees of the World,
by Christopher O'Toole and Anthony Raw, Blandford Books (Cassell), London, 192pp., 1994.
[A comprehensive and highly illustrated account for the layman of the fascinating natural histories of bees from around the world.]

Alien Empire: an Exploration of the Lives of Insects,
by Christopher O'Toole, BBC Books, London, 224pp., 1995.
[The book of the BBCtv series of the same name, this is a detailed account for the layman of the ecological importance of insects for the rest of life on earth.]

The Forgotten Pollinators,
by Stephen L. Buchmann and Gary Paul Nabhan, Shearwater Books, 320pp., 1997.
[An excellent account of just how we depend for 80% of our food on the pollination services of wild bees and other insects and just how much the life-sustaining relationships between bees and plants is threatened by human degradation of habitats.]

The Orchard Mason Bee: The Life History, Biology, Propagation and Use of a North American Native Bee,
by Brian L. Griffin, Knox Cellars Publishing Co., Washington State. 128pp, 1999
[An easy to read account of *Osmia lignaria*, the North American cousin of the European Red Mason Bee, *Osmia rufa*.]

Crop Pollination by Bees,
by Keith S. Delaplane and Daniel F. Mayer, CABI Publishing,
Wallingford, UK, 344pp, 2000.
[A comprehensive overview of bees as managed crop pollinators in temperate regions.]

Field Notes

	Date of first appearance of ♂♂	Date of first appearance of ♀♀	Date of first sealed nest	Date of last sealed nest
Year 1				
Year 2				
Year 3				
Year 4				
Year 5				

Date	Flowers Visited	
	♂♂	♀♀

Plate 1

A female Blue Orchard Mason Bee, Osmia lignaria.
© *Scott Bauer/USDA-ARS Photo Unit.*

Plate 2

A worker honeybee, Apis mellifera, at apple blossom, with nearly full pollen baskets.

© *Ken Preston-Mafham, Premaphotos Wildlife.*

Plate 3

A female Horn-faced Mason Bee, Osmia cornifrons, *with a full pollen load in her abdominal scopa, resting on a leaf.*
© *Karen Strickler.*

Plate 4

A worker of the European Garden Bumblebee, Bombus hortorum, *uses its long tongue to probe for nectar in the deep, tubular flower of a primrose,* Primula vulgaris. *North American bumblebees with equally long tongues include* Bombus *fervidus and* B. vagans. *In such species, tongues can be 75-80% of body length.*
© *Ken Preston-Mafham, Premaphotos Wildlife.*

Plate 5

Emerging from her 'quarry', a female of the European Red Mason Bee,
Osmia rufa, *bears a glistening pellet of mud between her jaws, ready for
use back at her nest.*
© *Ken Preston-Mafham, Premaphotos Wildlife.*

Plate 6

Carrying her ball of mud, a female of the European Red Mason Bee, *Osmia rufa* returns to her nest in an old garden cane. Note one of the pair of
stout horns beneath the antennae with which she presses her mud into
the desired shape inside the nest. You can also see the dense scopa or
fringe of specialized pollen-transporting hairs on the underside of her
abdomen.
© Dr Rod Preston-Mafham, Premaphotos Wildlife.

Plate 7

Four completed cells of the European Red Mason Bee, Osmia rufa, *each with a pearly white egg on its pollen store. Note the mud partitions between each cell. A section through the nest of* Osmia lignaria, *its North American close relative, would look identical.*
© Anthony Raw

Plate 8

Nearly full-grown larvae of the European Red Mason Bee, Osmia rufa, *feeding on pollen.*
© Anthony Raw

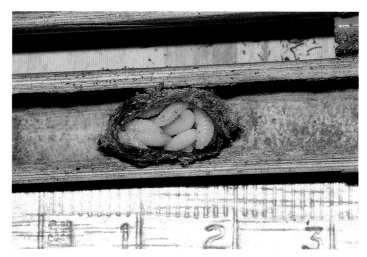

Plate 9

A pupal cocoon of the European Red Mason Bee, Osmia rufa, *opened to expose the larvae of the parasitic wasp,* Monodontomerus obscurus, *which have eaten the bee pupa. In North America, this wasp parasitizes the Blue Orchard Mason Bee,* Osmia lignaria, O. cordata *and the Alfalfa Leafcutter Bee,* Megachile rotundata.
© *C. O'Toole*

Plate 10

A female of the Alfalfa Leafcutter Bee, Megachile rotundata, *at alfalfa flowers,* Medicago sativa.

© *Karen Strickler.*

Plate 11

A trailer-mounted field shelter containing thousands of nests of the Alfalfa Leafcutter bee, Megachile rotundata, *in an alfalfa field, Cache Valley, Utah.*
© C. O'Toole

Plate 12

A female of a native North American mason bee, Osmia ribifloris, *which has potential as a managed pollinator of highbush blueberry. This female is feeding at flowers of barberry* (Berberis *sp.*).
© *Jack Dykinga, USDA-ARS Photo Unit.*

Plate 13

Nester kits for mason bees from the Oxford Bee Co. © Peter O'Toole

Plate 14
Nester kit for mason bees attached to wooden fence with plastic pipe bracket.
© Peter O'Toole